It's Another Ace Book from CGP

It's chock-full of questions that are carefully designed to make sure
you know all the <u>really important stuff</u>
about the 'Earth, Sun and Moon' in Year Five Science.

And we've had a really good stab at making it funny —
so you'll actually <u>want to use it</u>.

Simple as that.

CGP are just the best

The central aim of Coordination Group Publications is to produce
top quality books that are carefully written, beautifully
presented and marvellously funny — whilst always making sure
they exactly cover the National Curriculum for each subject.

And then we supply them to as many people as we possibly can,
as <u>cheaply</u> as we possibly can.

Buy our books — they're ace

Contents

Answers to the questions are on the back of the Pull-out Poster in the centre of the book.

Published by Coordination Group Publications Ltd.

Contributors:
Angela Billington BA (Hons), MPhil
Chris Dennett BSc (Hons)
Lindsay Jordan BSc (Hons)
Tim Major
Katherine Stewart BA (Hons)
Claire Thompson BSc
Tim Wakeling BA (Hons), GIMA
James Paul Wallis BEng (Hons)
Suzanne Worthington BSc (Hons)

ISBN 1-84146-279-9
Groovy website: www.cgpbooks.co.uk
Jolly bits of clipart from CorelDRAW
With thanks to NASA for the photographs on page 21.
Printed by Elanders Hindson, Newcastle upon Tyne.

Finding Out What You Know

Welcome to the Universe. The Earth seems like a pretty big place, but it's just a little planet spinning round a big star, called the Sun. Phew — it's just mind-blowing...

Q1   Here are a load of questions about the Earth, Sun and Moon. Fill in as many answers as you can. The idea is to see what you already know — don't worry if you can't do them all.

What I Know About the Earth, Sun and Moon

What shape is the Earth — flat and square, flat and round or football shaped?	....
Which is the biggest — the Sun, the Moon or the Earth?	....
When are shadows longer — at 12:00 midday or at 3:00 in the afternoon?	....
Does the Earth move round the Sun, the Moon or the planet Mars?	....
When it is daytime in England, which one of these countries is dark — Scotland, Wales or Australia?	....
Where does the Sun rise — in the East, West or South?	....
In Britain, is daytime in February longer, shorter or the same length as in June?	....
Name the missing season: Spring, Summer, _____ , Winter.	....
How long does the Earth take to move around the Sun — a day, a month, a year or a thousand years?	....
Do you always see the same side of the Moon from the Earth? (Yes or No)	....
How often do you see a full Moon — every day, every 28 days or every year?	....

Splurgle bargle blurgle?

Mork had no idea about the Sun, the Moon or the Earth.

What on Earth's going on?...

Don't worry about not knowing everything — you'll learn all this stuff as you go through the book. When you get to the end, you can have another go at the questions and see what you've learnt.

The Earth, Moon and Sun are Spheres

Some things (like pancakes) are round but <u>flat</u> — others (like balls) are round <u>whichever</u> way you look at them. The special word for ball-shaped things is 'sphere'.

Q1 (Circle) the right words in this sentence.

If you look at a coin from the top, it looks (ROUND / SQUARE) , but if you look at it from the side, it just looks like a (TRIANGLE / THIN LINE). This is because it's (ROUND / FLAT). A football is different. A football looks (FLAT / ROUND) no matter which way you turn it. Instead of saying 'football-shaped', scientists use the fancy word (SPHERICAL / CUBOID).

Sphere trivia
The word 'sphere' comes from the Greek word *sphaira*, which means 'ball'.

Q2 Some of the things in this table are flat, and some are spherical.
Finish off the table by writing 'flat' or 'spherical' next to each name.

Object	Flat or Spherical?	Picture
Earth		
Ping pong ball		
Coin		
Moon		
Biscuit		
CD		
Sun		

The Earth and the Moon and the Sun are kind of spherical. But they're not <u>perfect</u> spheres — they're only <u>roughly</u> ball-shaped.
(If they were exactly ball-shaped, there couldn't be any mountains.)

It's just round the corner.

The journey to the edge of the Earth was taking longer than planned.

The biscuits are round here — but flat there...

The problem with saying something's 'round' is that you could mean <u>coin</u>-shaped or <u>ball</u>-shaped.
The word '<u>spherical</u>' looks a bit tricky, but it's more accurate — and dead impressive if you use it.

The Earth, Moon and Sun are spheres

We know now that the Earth is <u>spherical</u> — but for quite a long time, people thought it was flat. It <u>seemed</u> flat to them, so they thought it <u>was</u> flat.

Q1 Fill in the blanks in these sentences. Choose the right words from the ball on the right. (You don't need to use all the words.)

We can't tell just by .... on it that the Earth is spherical.

It's only in the last 40 years that .... could be

taken of the Earth from ...., but we have known

for much longer than 40 years that the Earth is ....

> space
> spherical
> photographs
> standing
> aliens
> flat

Q2 Lancelot lived at a time when people thought the Earth was flat. Lesley lives now. Put each of the sentences from the box at the bottom of the page into one of their thought bubbles to show what Lancelot thinks and what Lesley thinks.

Lancelot

Lesley

The Earth <u>feels</u> flat, so it must be flat.

We can see that the Earth is spherical from satellite photos.

Ships can sail right round the Earth.

Astronauts went to the Moon and saw that the Earth is spherical.

It is impossible to go to the Moon.

Ships would fall off the edge of the Earth if they sailed too far.

Earth — the sphere on which I live...

Not just the Earth, but <u>all</u> the other planets are spherical too. It may seem a bit strange to think that you're walking around on a big ball — but that's the way it is.

The Size of the Earth, Moon and Sun

The Earth is enormous. It's <u>huge</u>. After you've done this page, you'll
know exactly how huge it is, so read on, be amazed, and enjoy...

Q1   Here's a picture of the Earth to scale.
Read the paragraph on the right and
then answer the questions below.

The Earth has a diameter of 12,700 km.
Britain is 940 km from top to bottom.
If the Earth were really only 10 cm
across, like this picture, then the Moon
would be only 3 cm across. The actual
diameter of the Moon is 3500 km.

a)   Find Britain on the picture of the
Earth and put a (circle) around it.

b)   Finish the sentence in the
white box to say what the
actual length of Britain is.

The length of Britain is ....

c)   Between the two red arrows at
the bottom of the picture, write
in the diameter of the Earth (the
real Earth, not the picture).

Richard thought this
would be a novel way
to arrive at his
brother's wedding.

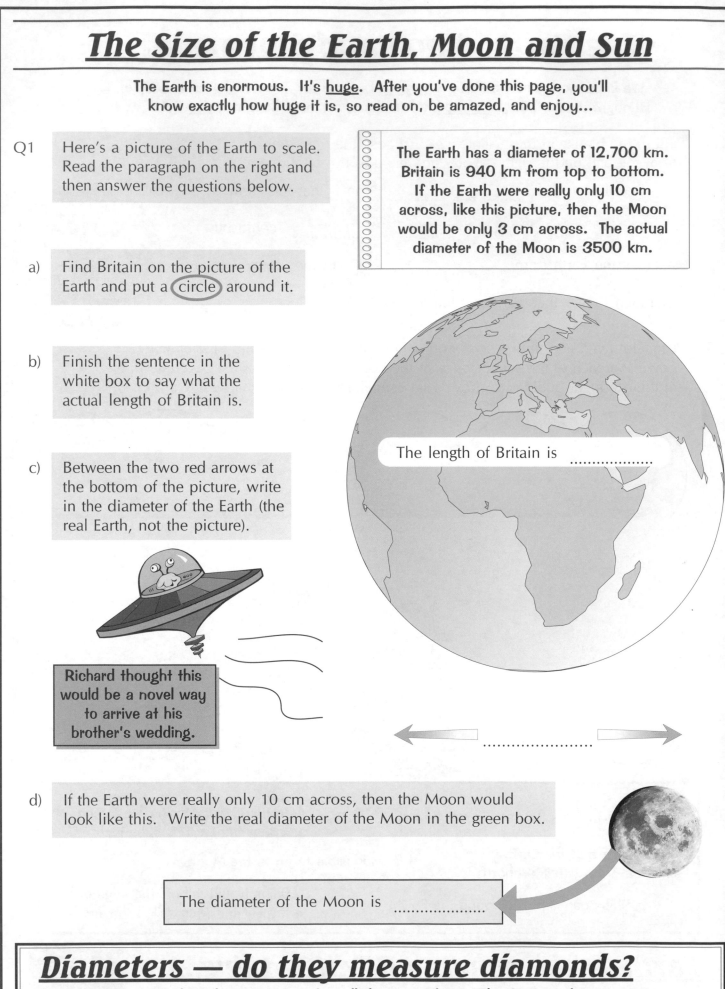

....

d)   If the Earth were really only 10 cm across, then the Moon would
look like this. Write the real diameter of the Moon in the green box.

The diameter of the Moon is ....

<u>Diameters — do they measure diamonds?</u>

Don't worry — you don't have to remember all those numbers. They're just there to give you an
idea of the <u>immense</u> size of the Earth. The Moon's not exactly small either, for that matter.

The Size of the Earth, Moon and Sun

Even if the Earth and Moon were as small as the pictures on page 4, the Sun would still be bigger than this page. In fact, it would be bigger than a <u>house</u> — it would be 17 metres from top to bottom, because the <u>actual distance</u> across the Sun is a whopping <u>1,392,000 km</u>.

Q1 Fill in this table with the distance across the Earth, the Moon and the Sun.

You might find it handy to look on the previous page for some of the answers.

DON'T look directly at the Sun. It can make you blind.

Object	Diameter
MOON	....
EARTH	....
SUN	....

Q2 Using some of the words in the blue boxes on the right, fill in the blanks to complete this sentence.

SHEEPDOG EARTH RUM TRUFFLE SUN MOON FOOTBALL

Out of the Earth, Moon and Sun, the .... is by far the biggest sphere, the .... is the next biggest and the .... is the smallest.

Q3 Circle the right words to finish off this paragraph about <u>size</u> and <u>distance</u>.

The Sun and Moon appear to be very small in the SKY / GROUND . This is because they are a long way away. An aeroplane up close looks TINY / HUGE . When you are at the other end of the runway it looks SMALLER / BIGGER — and when it is in the sky it looks TINY / ENORMOUS . The further away something is, the LARGER / SMALLER it looks. That's why a massive SPHERE / OVAL like the Sun looks like it's small.

Your trip around the Earth — plan-et well...

You wouldn't know it from looking, but the Sun is MUCH further away from us than the Moon is. And MUCH bigger. It's because it's so much <u>further away</u> that it looks about the same size.

The Size of the Earth, Moon and Sun

The Moon and the Sun are <u>really far away</u> — that's why they look so small.
You're about to find out exactly how far away the Sun and the Moon are.
I'll give you a clue — it's further than you could toss a pancake.

Q1 On the picture, and using the information on the notepad, fill in the distances from the Earth to a) the Moon and b) the Sun.

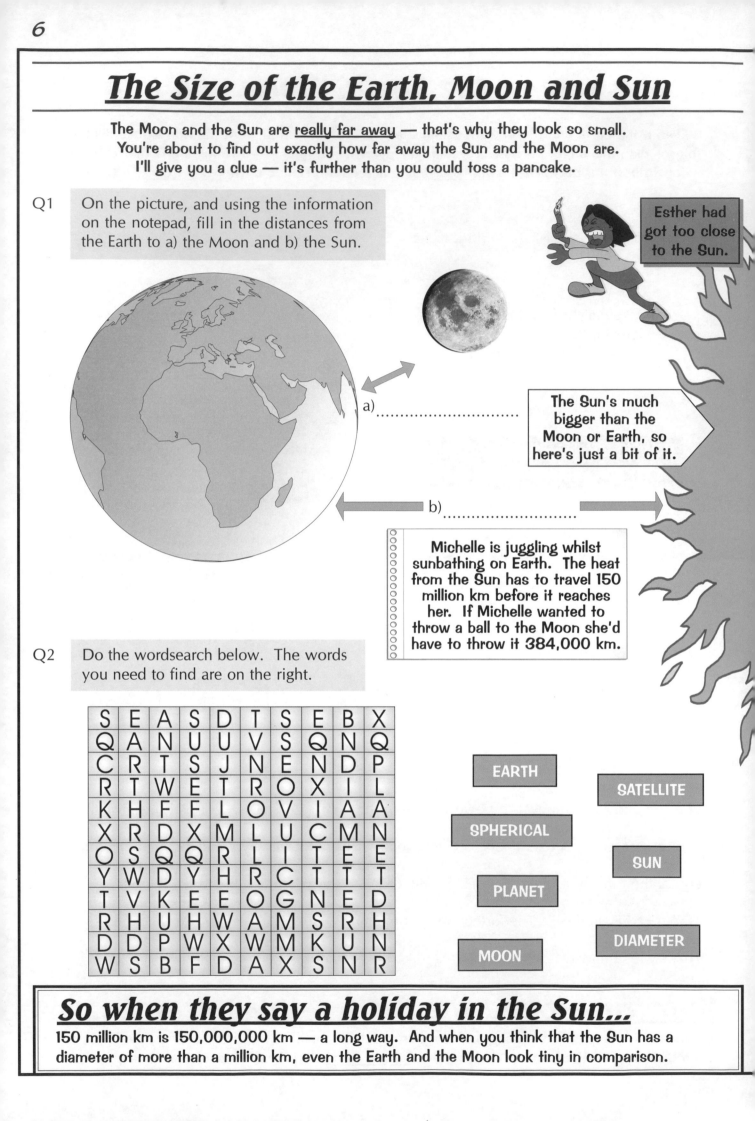

Esther had got too close to the Sun.

a) ....

The Sun's much bigger than the Moon or Earth, so here's just a bit of it.

b) ....

Michelle is juggling whilst sunbathing on Earth. The heat from the Sun has to travel 150 million km before it reaches her. If Michelle wanted to throw a ball to the Moon she'd have to throw it 384,000 km.

Q2 Do the wordsearch below. The words you need to find are on the right.

S	E	A	S	D	T	S	E	B	X
Q	A	N	U	U	V	S	Q	N	Q
C	R	T	S	J	N	E	N	D	P
R	T	W	E	T	R	O	X	I	L
K	H	F	F	L	O	V	I	A	A
X	R	D	X	M	L	U	C	M	N
O	S	Q	Q	R	L	I	T	E	E
Y	W	D	Y	H	R	C	T	T	T
T	V	K	E	E	O	G	N	E	D
R	H	U	H	W	A	M	S	R	H
D	D	P	W	X	W	M	K	U	N
W	S	B	F	D	A	X	S	N	R

EARTH

SATELLITE

SPHERICAL

SUN

PLANET

DIAMETER

MOON

So when they say a holiday in the Sun...

150 million km is 150,000,000 km — a long way. And when you think that the Sun has a diameter of more than a million km, even the Earth and the Moon look tiny in comparison.

The Sun Appears To Move

Do this experiment to find out what happens to the Sun during the day. Instead of measuring the direction of the Sun, you need to do it by measuring <u>shadows</u> — because looking at the Sun can make you blind.

SHADOW EXPERIMENT INSTRUCTIONS

1. Get someone to stand in the playground.
2. Draw around their feet with chalk, get them to step off and colour in the footprints so they don't rub off easily.
3. At 9 o'clock, get them to stand on the footprints and draw their shadow on the playground with chalk.
4. Get them to stand on the footprints again at 12 o'clock and 3 o'clock, drawing their shadow each time.

Everybody admired Mary's eye shadow collection.

Q1 For the experiment to work, you have to make it a fair test. Look at the six sentences below. Some are things you should do — put these in the "DO THESE" side of the table. Some are things you shouldn't do — put these in the "DON'T DO THESE" side of the table.

Make sure the person stands on the chalk marks each time.

Get the person to stand up straight each time you draw the shadow.

Let the person stand in a different place each time.

Write the time next to each shadow, so you know which is which.

Do the experiment on a cloudy day when there are no shadows.

Let the person move around so the shadow moves.

DO THESE	DON'T DO THESE

Space fact

The Sun is incredibly old — 4 500 000 000 years. But you don't need to worry — it isn't about to run out. The Sun will keep on going for another 5 000 000 000 years before it even begins to get short of fuel.

Shadows — bet you can't jump over yours...

You have a shadow when it's sunny because your body is <u>blocking</u> the sunlight off from a bit of the ground — leaving a dark bit shaped like you. BUT it's not always the same length.

MINI-PROJECT 1

The Sun Appears To Move

Now you actually get to <u>do</u> the experiment from page 7 — drawing chalk footprints on the playground and all that.

Q1 Carry out the experiment on page 7. Make sure you follow the things from the "DO THESE" side of the table and make sure you don't do the things from the "DON'T DO THESE" side.

Q2 Follow all the instructions below to finish off the picture.

Instructions

1) Fill in the tag to say who was standing in the playground.

2) Draw in the three shadows that you drew in chalk on the playground.

3) Label each shadow with the time that it was drawn.

This is ....

Q3 Are all the shadows in the same place? ....

Q4 What causes the shadows in the experiment? ....
....

COSMIC DISCO

The Sun was a groovy mover.

Q5 Why do the shadows move? (Circle the correct answer.)

Because a different part of the Sun is shining on them.

Because the person is moving.

Because the Sun is shining from different directions each time.

Q6 Does the Sun look as if it moves across the sky? ....

Planets moving — they don't need suitcases...

The Sun looks like it moves across the sky, but don't be fooled — it just <u>looks</u> like it's moving. In fact, the Sun stays still while the <u>Earth</u> does the moving. It's all on the next few pages.

The Spinning Earth

In the olden days, people didn't know that much about space and the planets.
Most people used to think that the Sun went <u>round</u> the Earth — because it looks as though the Sun <u>disappears</u> on one side of the Earth and moves to the other side where it <u>appears</u> again.
Nowadays we know that it's the <u>Earth</u> that's spinning, so it <u>looks</u> as if the Sun moves.

Q1   As the Earth spins, it looks as if the Sun is moving across the sky — but that doesn't mean that's what is <u>really</u> happening. Think about what happens when you're in a car or train — it looks as if everything <u>outside</u> is moving, when really <u>you're</u> the one that's moving.

Write T for true or F for false after each of these sentences.

a) If you're on a train and it looks like all the trees and houses go whizzing past you, it's the train that's standing still and the trees and houses that are moving.

b) If you're on a train and it looks like all the trees and houses go whizzing past you, it's the train that's moving and the trees and houses that are standing still.

c) If you're in a car and it looks like buildings are moving past your window, it is the car that's standing still and the buildings that are moving.

d) If you're on a playground roundabout and it looks like the rest of the world goes spinning past, it's the roundabout that's staying still and the playground that's moving.

e) If you're on a playground roundabout and it looks like the rest of the world goes spinning past, it's the roundabout that's moving and the playground that's staying still.

f) If you're on the Earth and it looks like the Sun rises and falls again every day, it's the Sun that is moving around the Earth.

g) If you're on the Earth, it looks like the Sun is going round the Earth, but it's not really moving. It's the Earth that's spinning.

Norma worried a lot about the Earth spinning a bit too fast.

The world is spinning — don't get too dizzy...

Don't always trust the way it looks — remember that it's the Earth that spins, not the Sun going around the Earth. Don't make the same mistake that scientists did hundreds of years ago.

The Spinning Earth

Light from the Sun can only reach <u>half</u> of the Earth at once, and as the Earth spins around, <u>different</u> parts of the world are in the light. That's what makes day and night happen.

Q1 The pictures below show Rodney in Britain and Bruce in Australia at different times of the day. Write each of the sentences under the picture that it describes.

It's evening for Bruce.   It's morning in Australia.

It's morning in Britain.   It's midday in Britain.

It's evening for Rodney.   It's midday for Bruce.

<u>So does that mean every day's a Sun day...</u>

If anyone asks you about how days and nights happen, try to think of the pictures on this page — and remember that the Earth spins all the way round <u>every day</u> and then it starts again.

The Spinning Earth

If you've got the hang of the last page, these questions'll be a doddle.

Q1   Take another look at the pictures on the last page and then answer these questions about them.

a) Which pictures show Bruce's day time?   .... , ... and ....

b) Which pictures show Rodney's day time?   .... , ... and ....

c) In picture A it has just become light for Rodney. Do you think it is his morning, lunchtime or evening?   ....

Q2   Fill in the blanks with words from the brackets.

Rodney's .... (day time / night time) is when Britain is facing the Sun

and his .... (day time / night time) is when Britain is not facing the Sun.

Q3   Fill in the blanks with either DAY TIME or NIGHT TIME.

When it's .... for Rodney in Britain,

it's .... for Bruce in Australia.

When it's .... for Bruce in Australia,

it's .... for Rodney in Britain.

That is __not__ a sword.

When your part of the Earth's in darkness, it's called __night time__ — not _knight_ time.

Q4   Put a tick next to the correct sentence.

When Rodney goes to bed, Bruce is going to bed as well. [ ]

When Rodney goes to bed, Bruce is getting up in the morning. [ ]

Time to eat dried fruit? — no, that's DATE time...

You know the Earth spins, and it is spherical — so only __half__ the world gets sunlight at any one time. That means that if it's __day time__ on one side of the Earth, it's __night time__ on the other side.

MINI-PROJECT 2

Sunrise to Sunset

This experiment is to find out where the Sun <u>rises</u> and <u>sets</u>. It's <u>dangerous</u> to look at the Sun, so the best way is to measure the direction of the <u>shadows</u>, with a <u>compass</u>.

To use a compass, hold it <u>flat</u> in the palm of your hand, and wait till the needle stops moving. Then carefully turn the compass so that so that the N is at the end of the arrow. Then the letters show you where North, South, East and West are.

Q1   For a bit of practice, work out where the sun is in each of these pictures. Read the direction <u>from</u> Bob's shadow <u>to</u> Bob — that tells you what direction the sun's in. I've done the first one for you.

Don't get confused — the arrow on his head has nothing to do with anything.

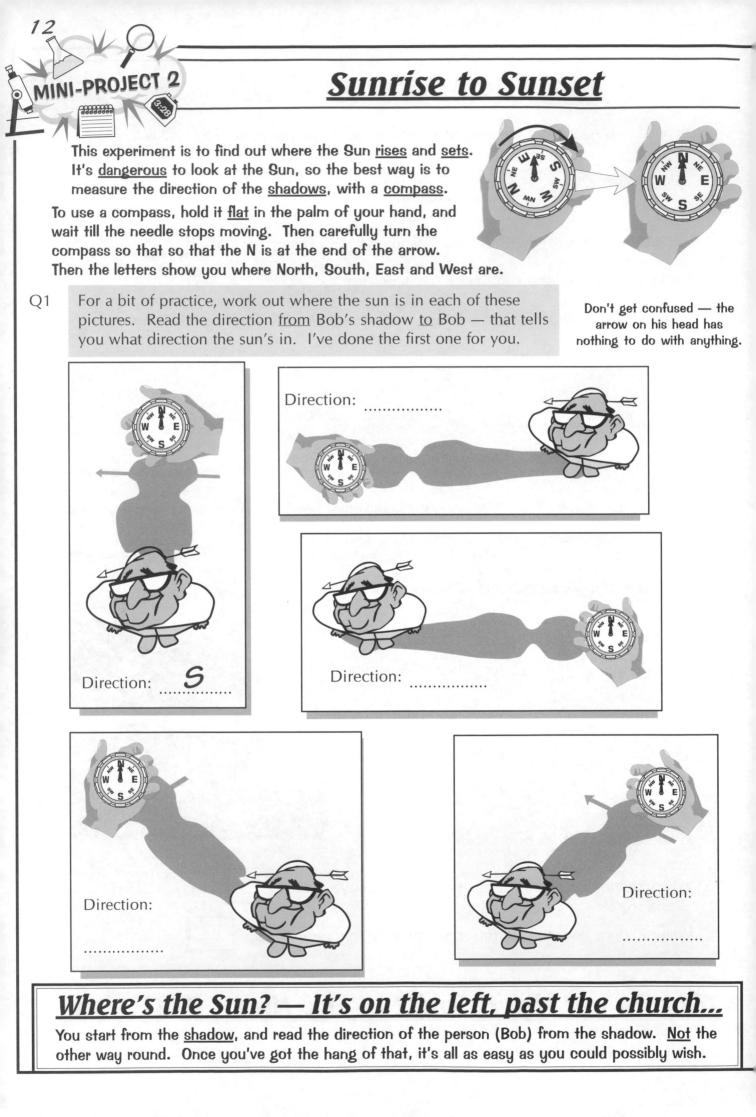

Direction: ....

Direction: _S_ ....

Direction: ....

Direction: ....

Direction: ....

Where's the Sun? — It's on the left, past the church...

You start from the <u>shadow</u>, and read the direction of the person (Bob) from the shadow. <u>Not</u> the other way round. Once you've got the hang of that, it's all as easy as you could possibly wish.

KS2 Science Answers — Earth, Sun and Moon

Page 15 Mini-Project 2 — Sunrise to Sunset

Q1:

	Date	Time	Direction of the Sun
Day 1	1st Jan	8:30	East
Day 2	2nd Jan	8:30	East
Day 3	3rd Jan	8:30	East

	Date	Time	Direction of the Sun
Day 1	1st Jan	4:00	West
Day 2	2nd Jan	4:00	West
Day 3	3rd Jan	4:00	West

Q2: The Sun rises in the **EAST** and sets in the **WEST**.

Page 16 Length of Days Over a Year

Q1: "Measure the time of the sunrise from the same place each time" should be ticked.

"Write down the time and date each time" should be ticked.

"Make sure your watch is accurate each time, by setting it to another accurate clock (like the speaking clock)." should be ticked.

Q2:

		January	February	March	April	May	June	July	August	September	October	November	December
AM	Sunrise	8.30	8:00	7.00	5.30	4.30	3.30	3.30	4.30	5.30	6:00	7.30	8.00
PM	Sunset	4.00	4.30	5.30	7.00	8.00	8.30	9.00	8.00	7.00	5.00	4.30	3.30

Page 17 Length of Days Over a Year

Q1 & Q2:

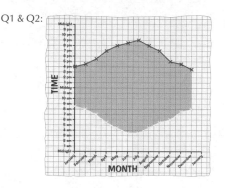

Q3: The days get **LONGER** from February to July and the days get **SHORTER** from July to January.

Page 18 Years and Days Depend on the Sun

Q1: A — True   B — True
    C — False   D — False
    E — True

Q2: a) You could put a stick in the ground and make a mark when the shadow is at its shortest — then measure the time it takes until the stick's shadow is at its shortest again.

b) It is easier to measure the length of time from one day to the next.

c) 365

d) You could measure the number of days between the longest day of one year and the longest day of the next year. (You would need to measure the number of hours of daylight in each day.)

Page 19 The Earth Orbits the Sun

Q1:

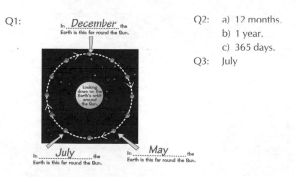

Q2: a) 12 months.
b) 1 year.
c) 365 days.

Q3: July

Page 20 Orbit of the Moon

Q1: i) A full Moon is when the **WHOLE** of one side of the Moon is visible. After a full Moon, the area we can see gets smaller. It looks like a **CRESCENT**.

When we can't see it at all, it's called a new Moon. Then it grows bigger until there is another **FULL MOON**. The Moon takes approximately **28 DAYS** to go from one new Moon to the next.

ii) By looking at the Moon's stages, **HUMANS** learned that it takes **28 DAYS** for the Moon to orbit the Earth. Orbit means to **'GO AROUND'** something. The Moon can sometimes be seen in the day, but it's **EASIER** to see at night.

Q2: a) TRUE   b) TRUE
    c) FALSE   d) TRUE

Q3: a) smaller   b) bigger

Page 21 Orbit of the Moon

Q1:

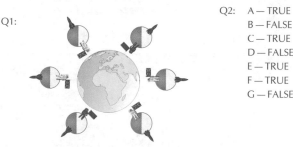

Q2: A — TRUE
B — FALSE
C — TRUE
D — FALSE
E — TRUE
F — TRUE
G — FALSE

Page 22 The Moon's Cycle

Q1: New Moon ➡ Full Moon ➡ New Moon

Q2: i) The full Moon stage — because you would be able to see all of the face of the Moon.

ii) The new Moon stage — because you would not be able to see the face of the Moon at all.

Q3: The boxes next to the binoculars and the telescope should be ticked.

Q4: Clouds.

Page 23 Revision Questions

Q1: The "tennis ball", "Earth", "Moon", "Sun" and "orange" boxes should be ticked.

Q2: a) 12,700 km.   b) Because it is far away.
c) The Moon.

Q3: The shadow would move throughout the day.

Q4: It's you that's spinning.

Q5: It's the Earth that's spinning.

Q6: a) Rodney   b) Daytime
c) Australia   d) No

Page 24 Revision Questions

Q7: East   South-West   South-East   South

Q8:

The Sun is in the East.	The Sun is setting.
The Sun is in the South.	The Sun is rising.
The Sun is in the West.	The Sun is at its highest point in the sky.

Q9: In **WINTER** days are short. The days get longer from **WINTER** to **SUMMER**. In **SUMMER** the days are long. The days get shorter from **SUMMER** to **WINTER**.

Q10: 1) The length of time it takes the Earth to orbit the Sun.
2) 12 months.

Page 25 Revision Questions

Q11: i) The Earth is football shaped.
ii) The Sun is the biggest.
iii) Shadows are longest at 3:00 pm.
iv) The Earth moves around the Sun.
v) It is dark in Australia.
vi) In the East.
vii) Daytime is shorter in February.
viii) Autumn.
ix) A year.
x) Yes.
xi) Every 28 days.

Q12: The boxes should be filled in with the amount of questions answered correctly.

KS2 Science Answers — Earth, Sun and Moon

Page 1 Finding Out What You Know

Q1: Shouldn't be marked, but here are the answers anyway.

i) The Earth is football shaped.

ii) The Sun is the biggest.

iii) Shadows are longest at 3:00 pm.

iv) The Earth moves around the Sun.

v) It is dark in Australia.

vi) In the East.

vii) Daytime is shorter in February.

viii) Autumn.

ix) A year.

x) Yes.

xi) Every 28 days.

Page 2 The Earth, Moon and Sun are Spheres

Q1: If you look at a coin from the top, it looks **ROUND**, but if you look at it from the side, it just looks like a **THIN LINE**. This is because it's **FLAT**. A football is different. A football looks **ROUND** no matter which way you turn it. Instead of saying 'football-shaped', scientists use the fancy word **SPHERICAL**.

Q2:
Earth — Spherical   Ping pong ball — Spherical

Coin — Flat   Moon — Spherical

Biscuit — Flat   CD — Flat

Sun — Spherical

Page 3 The Earth, Moon and Sun are Spheres

Q1: We can't tell just by **STANDING** on it that the Earth is spherical. It's only in the last 40 years that **PHOTOGRAPHS** could be taken of the Earth from **SPACE**, but we have known for much longer than 40 years that the Earth is **SPHERICAL**.

Q2:
Lancelot: The Earth feels flat, so it must be flat.

It is impossible to go to the Moon.

Ships would fall off the edge of the Earth if they sailed too far.

Lesley: We can see that the Earth is spherical from satellite photos.

Ships can sail right round the Earth.

Astronauts went to the Moon and saw that the Earth is spherical.

Page 4 The Size of the Earth, Moon and Sun

Q1: a)

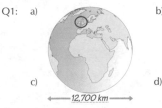

←— 12,700 km —→

b) The length of Britain is **940 km**.

c)

d) The diameter of the Moon is **3500 km.**

Page 5 The Size of the Earth, Moon and Sun

Q1: Moon — 3500 km   Earth — 12,700 km

Sun — 1,392,000 km

Q2: Out of the Earth, Moon and Sun, the **SUN** is by far the biggest sphere, the **EARTH** is the next biggest and the **MOON** is the smallest.

Q3: The Sun and Moon appear to be very small in the **SKY**. This is because they are a long way away. An aeroplane up close looks **HUGE**. When you are at the other end of the runway it looks **SMALLER** — and when it is in the sky it looks **TINY**. The further away something is, the **SMALLER** it looks. That's why a massive **SPHERE** like the Sun looks like it's small.

Page 6 The Size of the Earth, Moon and Sun

Q1: a) 384,000 km   b) 150 million km

Q2:

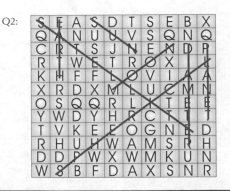

Page 7 Mini-Project 1 — The Sun Appears To Move

Q1:

DO THESE	DON'T DO THESE
Make sure the person stands on the chalk marks each time.	Let the person stand in a different place each time.
Get the person to stand straight each time you draw a shadow.	Do the experiment on a cloudy day when there are no shadows.
Write the time next to the shadow, so you know which is which.	Let the person move around so the shadow moves.

Page 8 Mini-Project 1 — The Sun Appears To Move

Q1: The experiment from page 7 should be done.

Q2: Here's my results using my friend Emily:

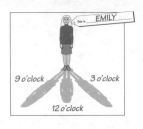

Q3: No.

Q4: The light from the Sun can't get through Emily's body so there is a bit of darkness where she stands.

Q5: "Because the Sun is shining from different directions each time" should be circled.

Q6: Yes.

Page 9 The Spinning Earth

Q1: b), e) and g) are **TRUE**, all others are **FALSE**.

Page 10 The Spinning Earth

Q1: A — It's morning in Britain.   B — It's midday in Britain.

C — It's evening for Rodney.   D — It's morning in Australia.

E — It's midday for Bruce.   F — It's evening for Bruce.

Page 11 The Spinning Earth

Q1: a) D, E and F show Bruce's daytime.

b) A, B and C show Rodney's daytime.

c) Morning.

Q2: Rodney's **DAY TIME** is when Britain is facing the Sun and his **NIGHT TIME** is when Britain is not facing the Sun.

Q3: When it's **DAY TIME** for Rodney in Britain, it's **NIGHT TIME** for Bruce in Australia. (Having DAY TIME and NIGHT TIME the other way round is also right.)

When it's **DAY TIME** for Bruce in Australia, it's **NIGHT TIME** for Rodney in Britain. (Having DAY TIME and NIGHT TIME the other way round is also right.)

Q4: "When Rodney goes to bed, Bruce is getting up in the morning" should be ticked.

Page 12 Mini-Project 2 — Sunrise to Sunset

Q1: Reading top to bottom: East, West, South-West, South-East

Page 13 Mini-Project 2 — Sunrise to Sunset

Q1: 1) Use a compass to measure the shadow's direction.

2) Make sure the compass is working properly.

3) Write down the time and date that you measured each shadow.

4) Make sure there are no bright lights making a different shadow.

Page 14 Mini-Project 2 — Sunrise to Sunset

Q1: Here are my pictures using the spare results from the bottom of page 15:

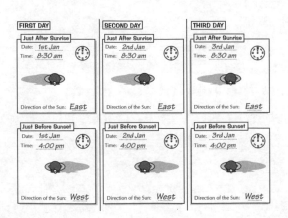

Sunrise to Sunset

To find out what direction the Sun _rises_ and _sets_ in, you work out the direction of the shadows just after the Sun rises, and just before it sets.

Q1 Read these 8 suggestions about measuring the directions of shadows. Some are great ideas, but some are seriously bad ideas. Choose the 4 good things to do and write them out on the lines underneath.

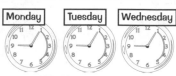 Never measure the shadows at 5 minutes past nine.

Measure the shadows at night.

 Use a compass to measure the shadow's direction.

Just guess the direction of each shadow.

Make sure it's a really cloudy day so you can't see the Sun.

Make sure the compass is working properly.

| Pedro was the only one who lost at shadow boxing. |

Write down the time and date that you measured each shadow.

Make sure there are no bright lights making a different shadow.

① ....

② ....

③ ....

④ ....

Compasses argue well — they always have a good point...

To give you a clue about what the good ways of doing the experiment are, think about making it a _fair test_ — that means making sure that _only one thing_ gets changed. It's dead important.

Sunrise to Sunset

Follow these instructions to do the experiment —
and don't forget the things you worked out on page 13.

INSTRUCTIONS:

Ask someone to stand up straight in the playground. Then draw a straight
line down the middle of the person's shadow with a piece of chalk.

Use a compass to measure the direction of the line you've drawn —
from the shadow to the person. That's the same as the direction
from the person to the Sun, which tells you where the Sun is.

This arrow points
to where the Sun is.

Do these measurements just after the Sun rises, and just before it sets
(or as near to sunrise and sunset as you can), on three days in a row.

This experiment works best in winter when sunset and sunrise happen close to the beginning and end of
the school day. You can do it in summer — you just won't get such a big difference in the shadows.

If you can't do the experiment, use my Spare Results from the bottom of the next page.

Q1   Each time you measure a shadow, draw a picture of it in one of the boxes. Write in the time
and the date, and the direction of the Sun (the direction from the shadow to the person).

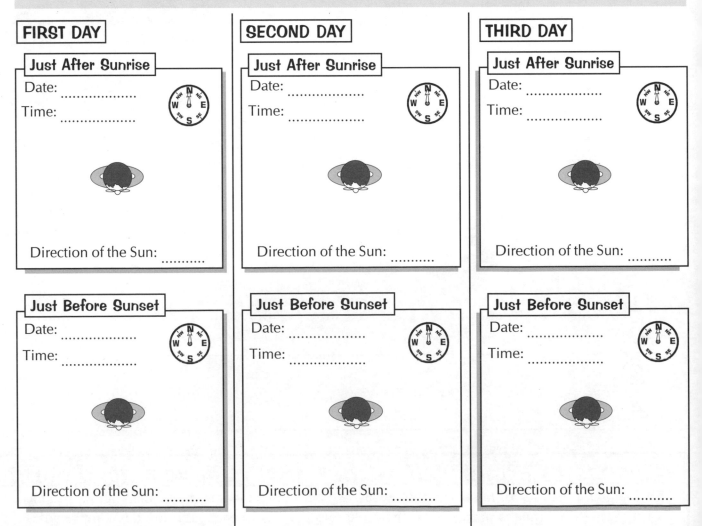

FIRST DAY

Just After Sunrise

Date: ....
Time: ....

Direction of the Sun: ....

Just Before Sunset

Date: ....
Time: ....

Direction of the Sun: ....

SECOND DAY

Just After Sunrise

Date: ....
Time: ....

Direction of the Sun: ....

Just Before Sunset

Date: ....
Time: ....

Direction of the Sun: ....

THIRD DAY

Just After Sunrise

Date: ....
Time: ....

Direction of the Sun: ....

Just Before Sunset

Date: ....
Time: ....

Direction of the Sun: ....

Sunrise to Sunset

Q1   Fill in these tables for sunrise and sunset with your results from the experiment.

SUNRISE TABLE

	Date	Time	Direction of the Sun
Day 1			
Day 2			
Day 3			

SUNSET TABLE

	Date	Time	Direction of the Sun
Day 1			
Day 2			
Day 3			

Unfortunately, Talvin's shadow couldn't get any further away from Talvin.

Q2   Choose from the words in Gwen's shadow to complete this sentence.

The Sun rises in the .... and sets in the ....

oven   fridge   East   West

The Sun's like a pudding — it rises and sets...

Phew — that's it. Remember that you need to get the arrow and the N on the compass lined up. Otherwise you've got no chance — it'll go completely pear-shaped. If it's a cloudy day and you can't see any shadows, then you're out of luck — you'll have to leave it for a sunnier day.

Length of Days Over a Year

Days are <u>longer</u> in summer, and <u>shorter</u> in winter. To find out exactly how <u>much</u> longer and shorter, you could measure the time that the sun rises and sets on the first day of <u>every month</u>.

Q1 Tick the right sentence from each of these pairs about how to do the experiment.

Measure the time of the sunrise from anywhere in the world each time. ☐ OR ☐ Measure the time of the sunrise from the same place each time.

Write down the time and date each time. ☐ OR ☐ Just write down the time.

Make sure your watch is roughly right at the beginning of the year, then don't check it at all. ☐ OR ☐ Make sure your watch is accurate each time, by setting it to another accurate clock (like the speaking clock).

Q2 I did the experiment and wrote my results in this notebook. Read through the results, and write out the times into the table at the bottom. I've done the first one for you.

These times are all in Greenwich Mean Time. In the summer, the clocks go forward an hour, but I took an hour off the time in the summer, so it didn't mess up the results.

Sun rise and set data for Manchester, in Greenwich Mean Time, for year 1999

On the 1st of January, the Sun rose at half past eight and set at four o'clock.

On the 1st of Febraury, the Sun rose at eight o'clock and set at half past four.

On the 1st of March, the Sun rose at seven o'clock and set at half past five.

On the 1st of April, the Sun rose at half past five and set at seven o'clock.

On the 1st of May, the Sun rose at half past four and set at eight o'clock.

On the 1st of June, the Sun rose at half past three and set at half past eight.

On the 1st of July, the Sun rose at half past three and set at nine o'clock.

On the 1st of August, the Sun rose at half past four and set at eight o'clock.

On the 1st of September, the Sun rose at half past five and set at seven o'clock.

On the 1st of October, the Sun rose at six o'clock and set at five o'clock.

On the 1st of November, the Sun rose at half past seven and set at half past four.

On the 1st of December, the Sun rose at eight o'clock and set at half past three.

		January	February	March	April	May	June	July	August	September	October	November	December
AM	Sunrise	8.30											
PM	Sunset	4.00											

Longer days? — the school day is pretty long already...

Putting the results in a <u>table</u> like this one makes them much easier to read and understand — and it takes up loads less room. Make sure you read all the times <u>carefully</u> when you're filling it in.

Length of Days Over a Year

The table on page 16 tells you what time the sun rose and set on the first day of each month of the year. To make it even _easier_ to see what's going on, you can plot the data in a _graph_.

Q1   On this graph paper, plot the times from the table on the last page. Mark a yellow cross for each sunrise time, then join them up. Do the same for the sunset times, but in red.

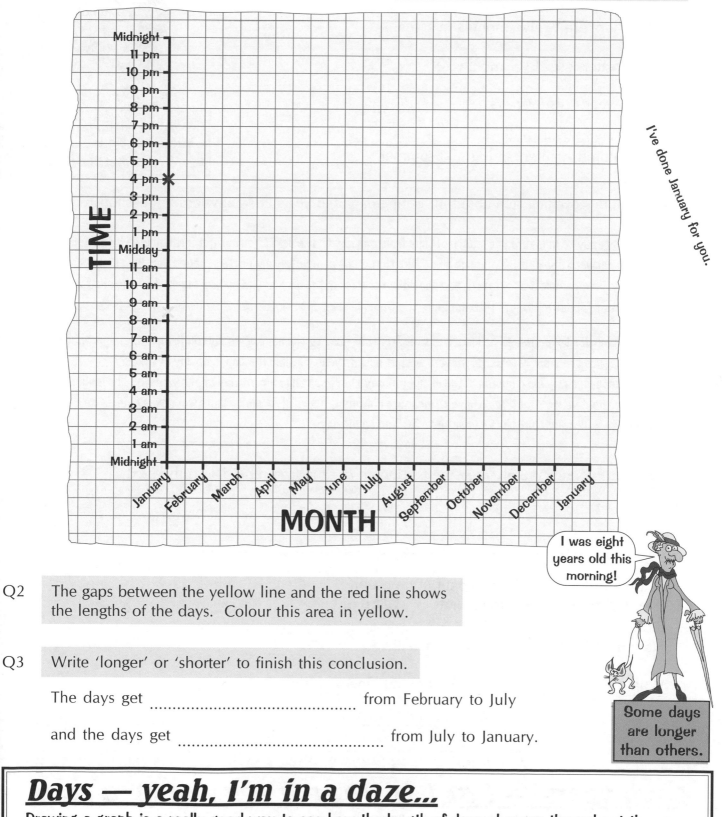

I've done January for you.

I was eight years old this morning!

Some days are longer than others.

Q2   The gaps between the yellow line and the red line shows the lengths of the days. Colour this area in yellow.

Q3   Write 'longer' or 'shorter' to finish this conclusion.

The days get .... from February to July

and the days get .... from July to January.

Days — yeah, I'm in a daze...

Drawing a graph is a really good way to see how the length of days changes throughout the year. It's a bit unfair, getting short days in winter. That's nature for you — it ain't all sweetness and light.

Years and Days Depend on the Sun

Years and days are both based on things to do with the Sun and the Earth moving.

Q1   Read these sentences and write 'true' or 'false' on the dotted line next to them.

(A)   The time between 2 of your birthdays is a year. ....

(B)   There are twelve months in a year. ....

(C)   Winter lasts 13½ months. ....

(D)   A year lasts 97 days. ....

(E)   A year has 4 seasons —
      autumn, winter, spring and summer. ....

North Pole

Bob and Sally agreed that winter was lasting an awfully long time this year.

Q2   Read all this exciting stuff about measuring days and years, then answer the questions underneath.

> It's pretty easy to measure the length of time from one day to the next. You can get a rough idea by measuring the time between one sunrise and the next. But that's not completely accurate because sunrise times change every day. To measure it accurately, you should put a stick in the ground and make a mark when the shadow is at its shortest (about midday). Then measure the time it takes until the stick's shadow is at its shortest again.
>
> It's much harder to measure the length of time from one year to the next. A really rough measurement would be to measure the time between 2 winters — but how do you tell when it's the first day of winter?
> A more accurate way is to measure the number of days between the longest day of one year and the longest day of the next year — but you'd have to measure how many hours of daylight there were every single day. Scientists have found out that a year lasts 365 and a bit days.

a)   How can you accurately measure the length of time from one day to the next?

....

....

b)   Is it easier to measure the length of time from
     one day to the next or the length of a year?   ....

c)   How many full days are there in a year?   ....

d)   What is an accurate way to measure the length of a year?

....

....

Long years — I get longer every y e a r ...

Trying to measure how long a year is would take ages... well, a whole year, anyway.
But because scientists have already worked it out, all you have to do is <u>learn</u> it — piece of cake.

The Earth Orbits the Sun

The Earth goes round the Sun in a huge circle then goes round it again, and again, and again — that's called <u>orbiting</u>. The Earth's orbit around the Sun always takes the <u>same</u> amount of <u>time</u>. I'm not going to tell you how long yet because it's one of the questions below.

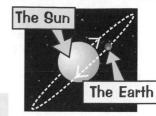

Q1   Complete the labels for the picture below by writing on the dotted lines.

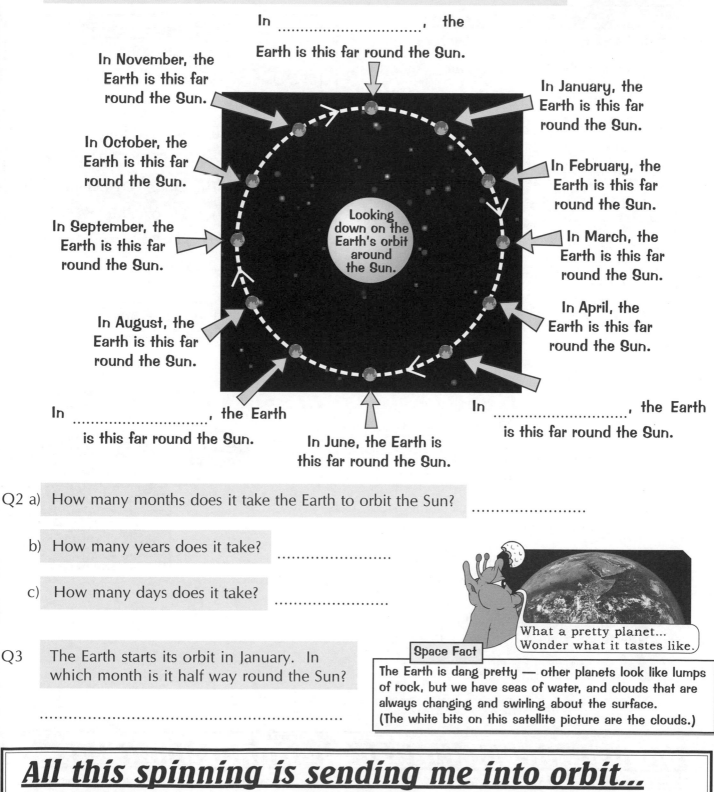

In ...., the Earth is this far round the Sun.

In November, the Earth is this far round the Sun.

In October, the Earth is this far round the Sun.

In September, the Earth is this far round the Sun.

In August, the Earth is this far round the Sun.

Looking down on the Earth's orbit around the Sun.

In January, the Earth is this far round the Sun.

In February, the Earth is this far round the Sun.

In March, the Earth is this far round the Sun.

In April, the Earth is this far round the Sun.

In ...., the Earth is this far round the Sun.

In June, the Earth is this far round the Sun.

In ...., the Earth is this far round the Sun.

Q2 a)   How many months does it take the Earth to orbit the Sun?   ....

b)   How many years does it take?   ....

c)   How many days does it take?   ....

Q3   The Earth starts its orbit in January. In which month is it half way round the Sun?

....

Space Fact

What a pretty planet... Wonder what it tastes like.

The Earth is dang pretty — other planets look like lumps of rock, but we have seas of water, and clouds that are always changing and swirling about the surface. (The white bits on this satellite picture are the clouds.)

<u>All this spinning is sending me into orbit...</u>

A year (365 days) is the amount of time it takes the <u>Earth</u> to spin round the <u>Sun</u>. So a year from today, the Earth will have spun round the Sun once. Just thinking about it makes me feel dizzy.

Orbit of the Moon

Hundreds of years ago, the Moon really puzzled people. They couldn't understand why it <u>changed</u> its <u>shape</u> during each month. Now we know it <u>doesn't</u> — it's just that sometimes, parts of it don't get any light from the sun, so they're too <u>dark</u> for us to see.

Q1 (Ring) the right words in the brackets to complete the information about the Moon.

The Stages of the Moon

A full Moon is when the (WHOLE / 72%) of one side of the Moon is visible. After a full Moon, the area we can see gets smaller. It looks like a (CARROT / CRESCENT). When we can't see it at all, it's called a new Moon. Then it grows bigger until there is another (FULL MOON / PANCAKE). The Moon takes approximately (28 YEARS / 28 DAYS) to go from one new Moon to the next.

Studying the Moon

By looking at the Moon's stages, (DOGS / HUMANS) learned that it takes (28 DAYS / 4 DAYS) for the Moon to orbit the Earth. Orbit means to (GO THROUGH / GO AROUND) something. The Moon can sometimes be seen in the day, but it's (EASIER / HARDER) to see at night.

As the Moon orbits the Earth, it spins so that the same side <u>always</u> faces the Earth.

This is really important.

Q2 Write TRUE or FALSE after each of these sentences.

a) From the Earth, you can only see one side of the Moon. ....

b) There are parts of the Moon that you can never see from Earth. ....

c) If an astronaut stood on part of the Moon not facing Earth, he would be able to see the Earth. ....

d) If an astronaut stood on part of the Moon facing the Earth, he would be able to see the Earth. ....

Neil had a sneaky way of seeing the Earth from anywhere on the Moon.

Q3 Say whether the Moon is getting bigger or smaller after a full Moon and after a new Moon.

a) Just after a full Moon: ....

b) Just after a new Moon: ....

I'm over the Moon to be learning about this...

The craters and stuff we can see on the Moon look the <u>same</u> all the time because it's spinning at just the <u>right speed</u> to make the <u>same bit</u> face us all the time. Of all the different speeds it could spin, it picked **EXACTLY** the one that keeps the same face facing us. That's pretty weird, I think.

Orbit of the Moon

The same side of the Moon <u>always</u> faces the Earth — which means you <u>never</u> see the other side.
We know what it looks like because <u>spacecraft</u> have taken photographs of it.

Q1   It's the year 2090 and Helen has gone to the Moon for a holiday. When she lands her
rocket, she can't see the Earth. She walks around the Moon and decides to stay on
the side facing the Earth. This picture shows six stages of the Moon's orbit. Draw
Helen and her rocket in the right place on the blank Moons to complete the picture.

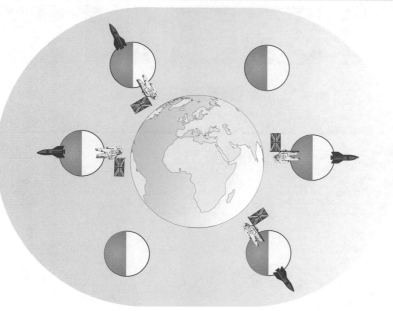

Helen realised it wasn't going to be
easy to find a burger restaurant.

Q2   Decide whether these sentences are TRUE or FALSE and cross out the wrong choice.

(A) In all of the pictures,
Helen can see the Earth.   True / False

(B) Helen can only see the Earth
for half the Moon's orbit.   True / False

(C) If Helen was sat on a huge
mountain, you could see
the mountain from Earth.   True / False

(D) Sometimes, if you
looked through a
powerful telescope,
you would see the rocket.   True / False

(E) A flying astronaut cow has
landed next to Helen. The cow
would be able to see the Earth.   True / False

(F) You would never be able to
see the rocket from the Earth.   True / False

(G) Helen has left her sandwiches in the rocket. We
could see her while she is rummaging in her rocket.   True / False

| Space Fact |
The Moon is the only natural object in space that people have visited. Twelve men
(no women — yet) have walked on it. This photo is the footprint of Neil Armstrong,
the first man on the Moon. It's still there because the Moon has no wind or rain.

What comes before astro-one — astro naut...

By now you should have the idea. The Moon goes <u>around</u> the Earth, but it also <u>spins</u> so that the
same side always faces the Earth. That's why you see the craters in the same place all the time.

The Moon's Cycle

The Moon's cycle is the 28 days from <u>new Moon</u> to the next <u>new Moon</u>.

Q1 Use the descriptions of full Moon and new Moon to write FULL or NEW in the blanks below.

Day 1

A <u>full Moon</u> is when the whole of one side of the Moon is visible.

A <u>new Moon</u> is when none of the Moon can be seen.

Day 28

.... Moon   .... Moon   .... Moon

Q2 What stage of the Moon would be <u>best</u> for studying it? Why?

....

....

What stage of the Moon would be <u>worst</u> for studying it? Why?

....

....

Neil began to suspect that someone had got to the Moon before him.

Q3 Put a tick by the equipment that would help you see the Moon's surface.

Cheese ☐

Telescope ☐

Sunglasses ☐

Binoculars ☐

Q4 You want to study the Moon tonight, and it's at the best stage for studying it. What might stop you being able to see the Moon?

....

Why's the Moon full? — too much Milky Way...

When people say "Once in a blue Moon" they mean not very often. A blue Moon happens when you get two full Moons in one month — the second one's called a blue Moon. Blue Moons don't happen very often, but in 2000 it happened twice in one year — that's really, really unusual.

Revision Questions

Check what you've learned by getting stuck into this little lot. On your marks... get set...

GO.

Q1 Which of these things are roughly spherical (ball-shaped)? Tick the ones that are.

pancake ☐   Earth ☐   elephant ☐

tennis ball ☐   Moon ☐   orange ☐

tea cup ☐   coin ☐   Sun ☐

Q2 a) What is the diameter of the Earth — 12,700 mm, 12,700 km or 12,700 m ? ....

b) Why does the Sun look really small in the sky? ....

c) Which is closer to the Earth — the Sun or the Moon? ....

Q3 If you stood still in your garden for a whole day, would your shadow point in the same direction or would it move throughout the day?

....

....

There was no doubt Hannah would win the Olympic Freestyle Shadow Championships again this year.

Q4 When you're on a roundabout, and it looks as if the park is spinning around you, is it you that's spinning or the park?

....

Q5 When you see the Sun rise every morning, move across the sky and set every evening, is it the Sun that's moving round the Earth, or is it the Earth that's spinning?

....

Q6 Here's a picture of Rodney in Britain and Bruce in Australia.

a) Who's on the side of the Earth facing the Sun? ....

b) Is Rodney in daytime or night time? ....

c) Where is it night time — Britain or Australia? ....

d) Is Australia facing the Sun or not? ....

Rodney

Bruce

People think Australia's upside down — it's not true...
So, the Earth's <u>round</u>, but looks <u>flat</u>, and the Sun's <u>huge</u>, but looks <u>small</u>. Looks can be deceptive.

Revision Questions

Keep at it — if you can do **all** the questions on these two pages,
then you know **all** the stuff in this book.

Q7 Look at these pictures of me measuring my dog's shadow.
Under each picture, write what compass direction the Sun is in.

....

Q8 Draw a line from the position of the Sun
to the description of what's happening.

POSITION

The Sun is in the East.

The Sun is in the South.

The Sun is in the West.

DESCRIPTION

The Sun is setting.

The Sun is rising.

The Sun is at its highest point in the sky.

Frank's sunglasses really were <u>sunglasses</u>.

Q9 Write 'winter' or 'summer' in the gaps to finish off these sentences.

In .... days are short. The days get longer from

.... to .... In .... the days are

long. The days get shorter from .... to ....

Q10 How long is a year? Choose the two right answers, and write them out on the dots.

The length of time it takes the Moon to orbit the Earth.

12 months.

24 months.   3 seasons.

The length of time it takes the Sun to orbit the Moon.

12 seasons.

The length of time it takes the Earth to orbit the Sun.

10 months.

1) ....

2) ....

....

<u>4 seasons a year — football, cricket, rugby and tennis...</u>

Don't stop now — you're nearly home and dry. By now you should know about everything you
need to know about the <u>Earth, Moon and Sun</u>. Look back at anything you're not too sure about.

Revision Questions

This is the table from page 1. You've already seen all the answers somewhere
in this book — so you shouldn't have <u>too</u> many problems.

Q11   Fill in this table. Remember, you can look back through the book if you get stuck.

What I Know About the Earth, Sun and Moon

What shape is the Earth — flat and square, flat and round or football shaped?	....
Which is the biggest — the Sun, the Moon or the Earth?	....
When are shadows longer — at 12:00 in the afternoon or at 3:00 in the afternoon?	....
Does the Earth move round the Sun, the Moon or the planet Mars?	....
When it is daytime in England, which one of these countries is dark — Scotland, Wales or Australia?	....
Where does the Sun rise — in the East, West or South?	....
In Britain would daytime in February be longer, shorter or the same as daytime in June?	....
Name the missing season: Spring, Summer, ____ , Winter.	....
How long does the Earth take to move around the Sun — a day, a month, a year or a thousand years?	....
Do you always see the same side of the Moon from the Earth? (Yes or No)	....
How often do you see a full Moon — every day, every 28 days or every year?	....

Q12 a) Get your teacher to tell you the answers. How many did you get right?

  b) Look back at the start of the book and mark your answers on page 1. How many did you get right last time?

  c) Take away your answer for b) from your answer to a).

You're now this much cleverer. Hurrah.

If you did worse this time than before, you must be having a bad day — have another go tomorrow.

<u>Fill in the gaps in the table — before your food falls through...</u>

You should be an <u>expert</u> on this stuff by now. Three whole revision pages and you're still smiling. ☺
Well, you're still <u>reading</u>, anyway. Fantastic. I reckon it's about time to go and put your feet up.

Index